My First Five Years

~ *Illustrated by* ~

Tracey Moroney

Victoria Avenue
PAPER COMPANY

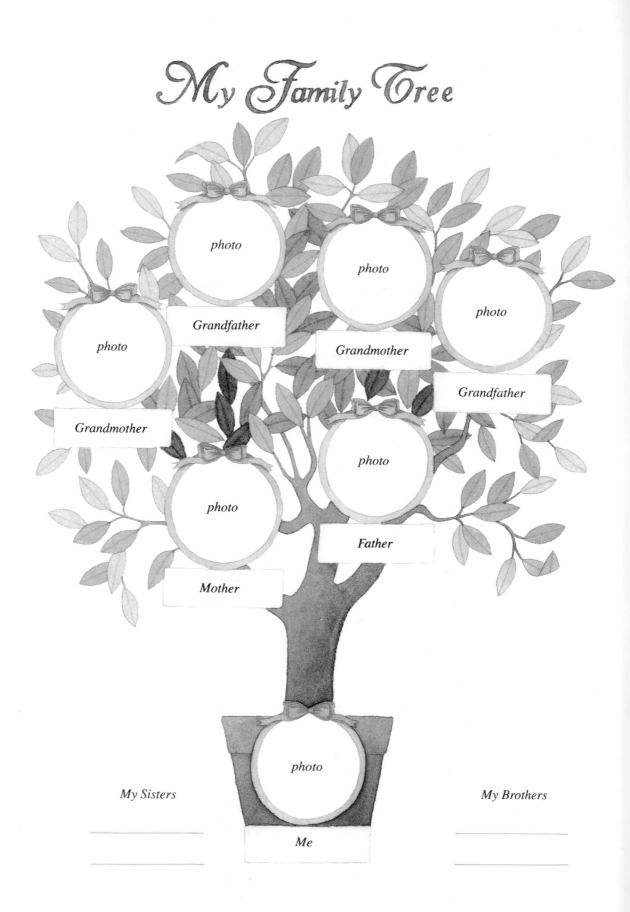

My Family Tree

photo

photo

photo

photo

Grandfather

Grandmother

Grandfather

photo

Grandmother

photo

photo

Father

Mother

photo

My Sisters

My Brothers

Me

Me at Six Months

photo

My weight _____

My length _____

My Favourite Things

Toys _____

Games _____

Songs _____

Food _____

Special Ways

_____

_____

_____

Bedtime

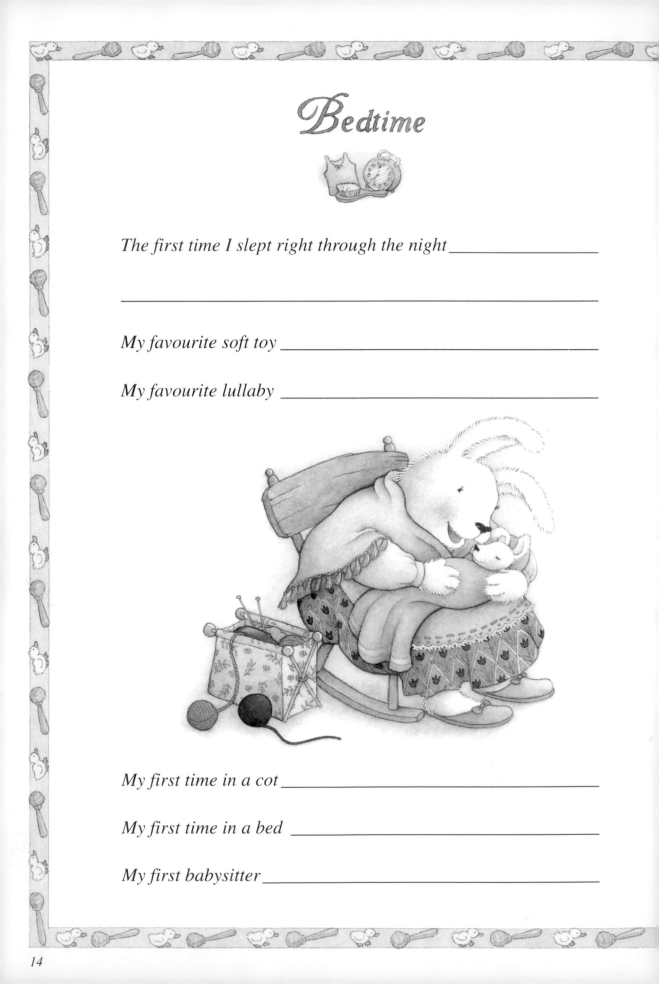

The first time I slept right through the night _____

_____

My favourite soft toy _____

My favourite lullaby _____

My first time in a cot _____

My first time in a bed _____

My first babysitter _____

Bathtime

I first started to enjoy my bath at (age) _____

My favourite bath toys _____

My favourite bath games _____

_____

How I react to a shampoo _____

The first time I went in the big bath _____

Me at Nine Months

My weight _____

My length _____

photo

My Favourite Things

Toys _____

Games _____

Books and songs _____

Food _____

Special Ways

_____

_____

_____

The First Time I...

Smiled _____

Gurgled _____

Laughed _____

Rolled over _____

Sat up by myself _____

Crawled _____

Stood up, holding on to something _____

Mealtime

My first solid food was _____

I was weaned at the age of _____

The first time I drank from a cup _____

My favourite foods _____

_____

_____

_____

My pet hates _____

_____

_____

_____

_____

The first time I held a spoon by myself _____

My First Christmas

Where I spent it _____

Who was there _____

How I reacted _____

What I ate and drank _____

What I enjoyed most _____

My favourite presents _____

_____

_____

_____

Teething

First tooth _____

Second tooth _____

Third tooth _____

Fourth tooth _____

Fifth tooth _____

Sixth tooth _____

Seventh tooth_____

Eighth tooth _____

Ninth tooth _____

Tenth tooth _____

Eleventh tooth _____

Twelfth tooth _____

Thirteenth tooth _____

Fourteenth tooth _____

Fifteenth tooth_____

Sixteenth tooth _____

Seventeenth tooth _____

Eighteenth tooth _____

Nineteenth tooth _____

Twentieth tooth _____

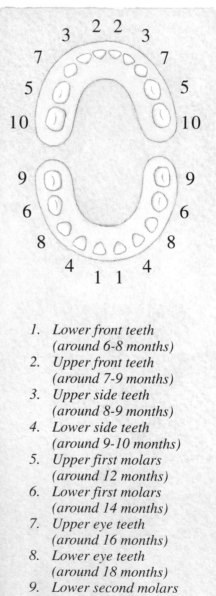

1. Lower front teeth
   (around 6-8 months)
2. Upper front teeth
   (around 7-9 months)
3. Upper side teeth
   (around 8-9 months)
4. Lower side teeth
   (around 9-10 months)
5. Upper first molars
   (around 12 months)
6. Lower first molars
   (around 14 months)
7. Upper eye teeth
   (around 16 months)
8. Lower eye teeth
   (around 18 months)
9. Lower second molars
   (around 22-24 months)
10. Upper second molars
    (around 24-26 months)

My First Birthday

How I celebrated it _____

Who else was there _____

My presents included _____

The ones I liked best _____

Other comments _____

_____

_____

_____

Me at One

photo

My weight _____

My height _____

My Favourite Things

Toys _____

Games _____

Books and songs _____

Food _____

Special Ways

_____

_____

_____

The First Time I...

Waved goodbye _____

Clapped hands _____

Walked holding onto furniture _____

Stood up by myself _____

Walked unaided _____

Wore shoes _____

Got my hair cut _____

Me at Eighteen Months

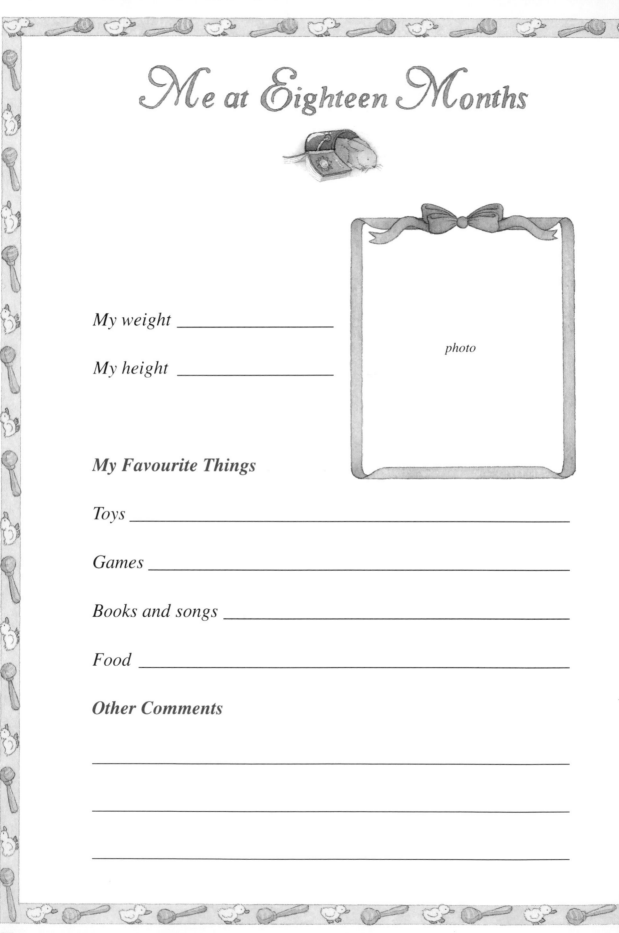

My weight _____

My height _____

My Favourite Things

Toys _____

Games _____

Books and songs _____

Food _____

Other Comments

_____

_____

_____

Special Outings

Where I went _____

What I did _____

What I enjoyed most _____

Other comments _____

_____

_____

_____

My Second Birthday

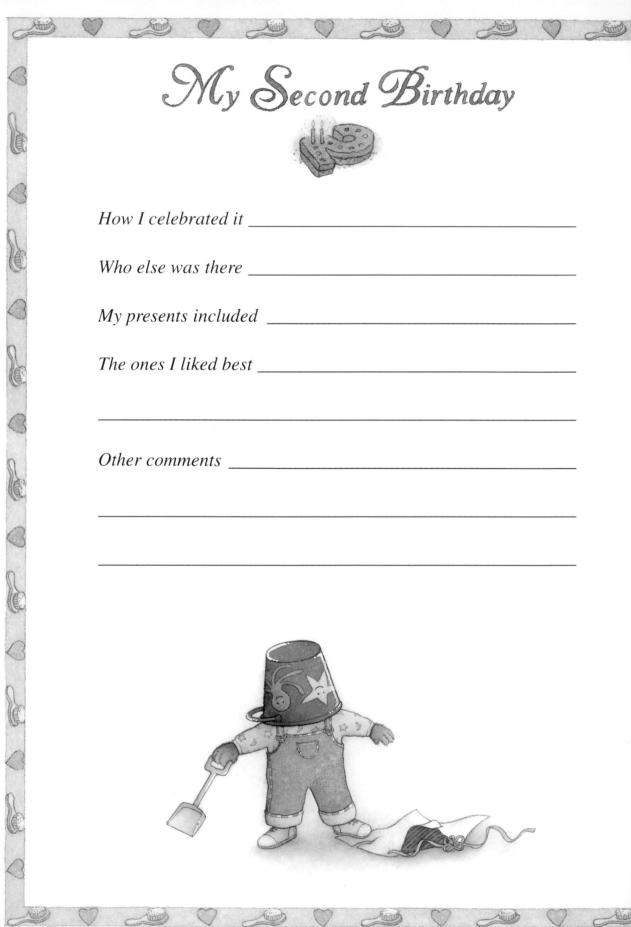

How I celebrated it _____

Who else was there _____

My presents included _____

The ones I liked best _____

_____

Other comments _____

_____

_____

Me at Two

photo

My weight _____

My height _____

My Favourite Things

Toys _____

Games _____

Books and songs _____

Food _____

Other Comments

_____

_____

_____

My Third Birthday

How I celebrated it _____

_____

_____

Who else was there _____

_____

_____

What I enjoyed most _____

My favourite presents _____

_____

_____

Other comments _____

_____

_____

_____

Me at Three

photo

My weight _____

My height _____

My Favourite Things

Toys _____

Games _____

Books and songs _____

Food _____

TV shows _____

Other Comments

_____

_____

_____

Kindergarten

My first day _____

Name of kindergarten _____

What I like _____

What I don't like _____

Things I've learnt _____

My teacher _____

Other comments _____

_____

My Fourth Birthday

How I celebrated it _____

Who else was there _____

_____

What I enjoyed most _____

_____

My favourite presents _____

_____

Other comments _____

_____

Me at Four

My weight _____

My height _____

My Favourite Things

Toys _____

Games _____

Books and songs _____

Food _____

TV shows _____

Other Comments

_____

_____

_____

photo

My Drawings

My Fifth Birthday

How I celebrated it _____

Who else was there _____

What I enjoyed most _____

My favourite presents _____

_____

Other comments _____

_____

_____

Me at Five

photo

My weight _____

My height _____

My Favourite Things

Toys _____

Games _____

Books and songs _____

Food _____

TV shows _____

Other Comments

_____

_____

My First Day at School

Date _____

Name of school _____

My teacher's name _____

What I liked _____

What I didn't like _____

What I had for lunch _____

_____

_____

What I learned _____

_____

_____

Other comments _____

_____

_____

More Drawings

Me and My Family

My Height

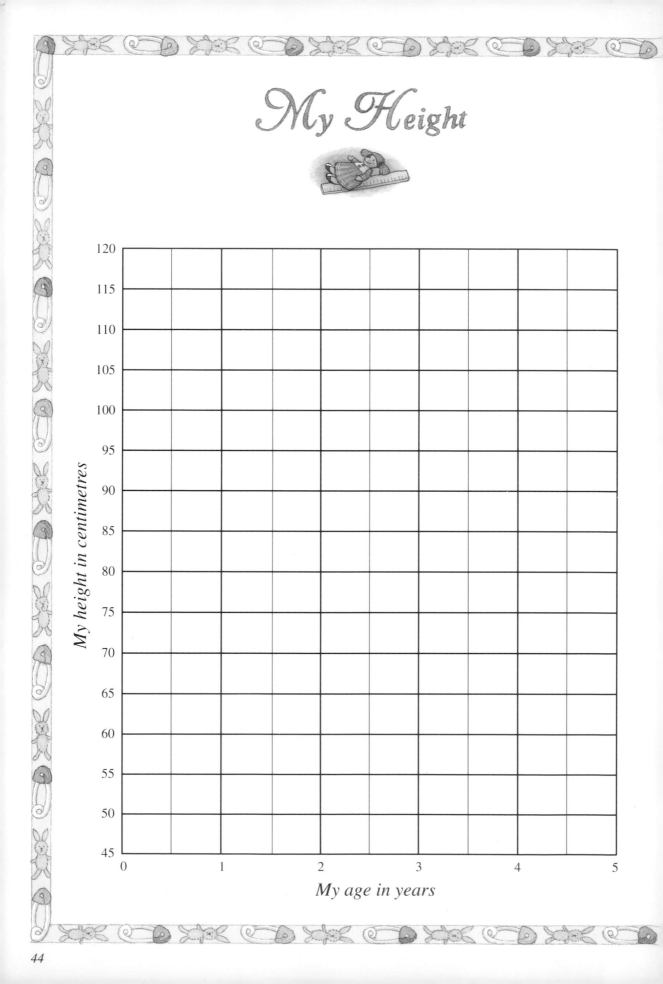

My height in centimetres

120
115
110
105
100
95
90
85
80
75
70
65
60
55
50
45

0　　　　1　　　　2　　　　3　　　　4　　　　5

My age in years

My Weight

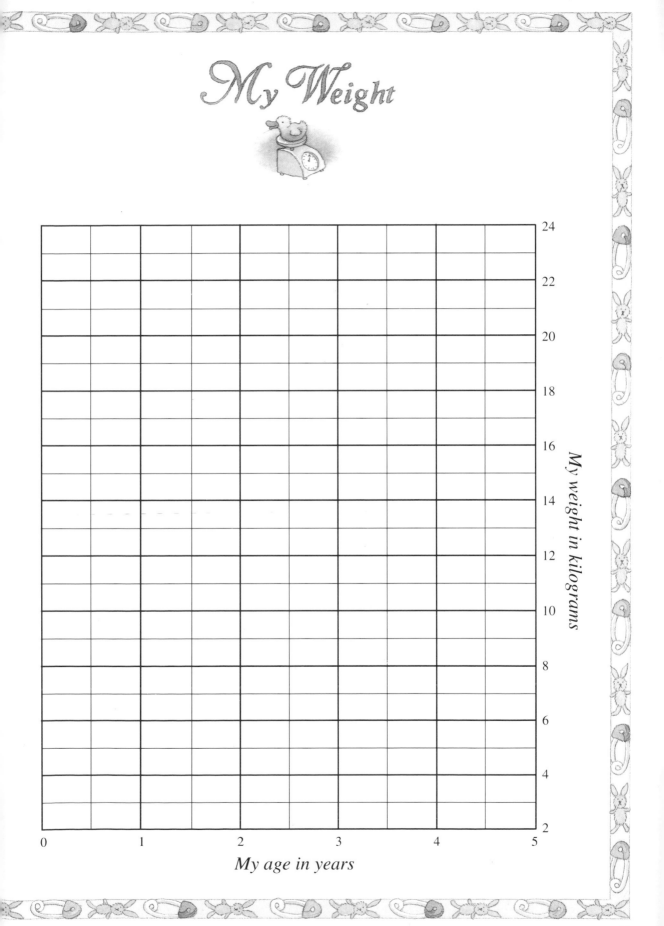

My weight in kilograms

My age in years

My Medical Records

Date   Vaccination

_____   _____

_____   _____

_____   _____

_____   _____

_____   _____

_____   _____

Blood group _____

Allergies _____

Local doctor _____ Tel _____

Specialist _____ Tel _____

Other _____ Tel _____

Childhood illnesses _____

_____